Gail lives in Milwaukee, Wisconsin, with her husband, Steve. They have four wonderful sons, four beautiful daughters-in-law and eight awesome grandchildren. Gail's favorite pastime is playing games with her family. She loves the outdoors, pickleball, tennis and volleyball. She has been told that she can turn anything into a competition, which she attributes to the fact that she was raised with five very competitive brothers.

I'M Not Scary

Gail Storvik

AUSTIN MACAULEY PUBLISHERS™
LONDON • CAMBRIDGE • NEW YORK • SHARJAH

Copyright © Gail Storvik (2021)

Ordering Information
Quantity sales: Special discounts are available on quantity purchases by corporations, associations, and others. For details, contact the publisher at the address below.

Publisher's Cataloging-in-Publication data
Storvik, Gail
I'm Not Scary

ISBN 9781647503451 (Paperback)
ISBN 9781647503444 (Hardback)
ISBN 9781647503468 (ePub e-book)

Library of Congress Control Number: 2021905666

www.austinmacauley.com/us

First Published (2021)
Austin Macauley Publishers LLC
40 Wall Street, 33rd Floor, Suite 3302
New York, NY 10005
USA

mail-usa@austinmacauley.com
+1 (646) 5125767

I would like to dedicate this book to my amazing, beautiful granddaughter, Lakelyn. Her spirit and determination have helped me realize that miracles do indeed happen.

I would like to thank my husband, Steve, for his support and belief in this book. He is truly an amazing father and grandfather. His encouragement means the world to me. I would like to thank God for bringing our sweet Lakelyn into all of our lives. She never ceases to amaze us all. I also need to acknowledge Erik and Paige, who are the most outstanding parents to our dear Lakelyn. They have helped her surpass *every* obstacle put in her path. When doctors told them, "She will never…" Erik and Paige answered with, "Yes, she will." And she *has*! It has been tough but they never give up and I love them for that. Lastly, I want to thank Austin Macauley Publishers for giving me a platform to help others feel comfortable greeting special needs children.

One morning when dad, mom, little brother, and
I woke up,
mom said we were out of milk, in fact,
we didn't have a cup.

"Out for breakfast for us," said dad as we brushed
our teeth and dressed.
Our favorite spot for pancakes but what
happened there, you could
never have guessed.

As mom and dad ate their pancakes, brother &
I played around,
till a girl from another table
dropped her plate on the ground.

At me she was looking and she pointed with fear ...
"That girl looks scary,"
was all we could hear.

"Me? scary?" I thought, why, this cannot be true.
I'm just a little kid, like my little brother and like you.

"Why does she think that?" I signed to my mom.
I wanted to cry but my dad said, "Stay calm."
"That little girl doesn't know you,"
he said with a smile.
Let's go say, "hi" and we walked
down the aisle.

"My name is Lakelyn," I signed to the girl.
"We both have pretty dresses," and
I gave mine a twirl.
My dad gave me a hug as he shook
her dad's hand.
He said, "Different is not scary but
can be hard to understand."

"Let me help," said my dad, "to teach others
that what they see, may look scary at first
but I hope you'll agree ..."
When you know what is different
maybe you can understand,
not everyone is the same, I guess
that's how God has it planned.

Lakelyn was born different than you
and than me.
She was born with small eyes, she can't
hear and she can't see.
Well, she sees very little but
she tries very hard to
not let that stop her from
playing ball in her yard.
She wants to have fun with friends, just like you.
She gets happy, she gets sad, she even gets
mad at her little brother too.

So, next time you see someone not
looking quite right,
Don't be scared and say hello, you will
find out they don't bite.
They are kids, just like you.
They want to have fun. They want to
have friends with to skip,
jump, and run.

Lakelyn is sweet, strong, and smart,
she would make a great friend
because she has a huge heart.

Then the little girl smiled at me and I smiled at her.
She twirled her dress and I twirled mine more.
"I am not scary," I signed
"and I hope you can see ...
that I'm a lot like you and you're a lot like me."

CPSIA information can be obtained
at www.ICGtesting.com
Printed in the USA
LVHW071621110621
689684LV00036B/2808